Canada's #1 Educational Resource

Reading • Math • More
Workbook

Grade **2**

Table of Contents

Elaine J. Kenny
Editors
Lisa Penttilä
Vin Sriniketh

Layout & Design
Michael P. Brodey

Canadian Curriculum Press
is an imprint of Telegraph Road

12 Cranfield Road,
Toronto, Ontario, Canada
M4B 3G8

©2017 Telegraph Road
ALL RIGHTS RESERVED
ISBN 978-1-4876-0161-4

For special bulk purchases, please contact
sales@telegraph-rd.com

For other inquiries, please contact:
inquiries@telegraph-rd.com

Printed in China

Dear Parents,

Welcome to the Grade 2 Workbook. Every colourful page is chock-full of exercises, games, and puzzles that reinforce the main concepts taught in Grade 2, plus colourful illustrations that stimulate a sense of fun.

The activities provide language and math curriculum practice that can be used as reinforcement during the school year, as summer preparation for an upcoming grade, or as review between grades.

Practice is essential in helping children become confident learners, but remember that all children learn at their own rate. As parents, we can help by setting a relaxed tone for learning time, praising our children's efforts, and stopping when they show signs of being tired.

Parents, the activities in this book will challenge your Grade 2 children and provide them with important practice while the imaginative activities means they'll have fun completing every page!

Finally, a big thank you to the teachers and kids who field-tested the workbook.

Sincerely,

Elaine J. Kenny

Elaine J. Kenny, B.P.H.E., B.Ed.

We acknowledge the financial support of the Government of Canada through the Canada Book Fund (CBF) for our publishing activities.

Canadian Heritage   Patrimoine canadien   Canada

SKIP COUNTING BY 2S, 5S, AND 10S

Fill in the blanks to count the palm trees.

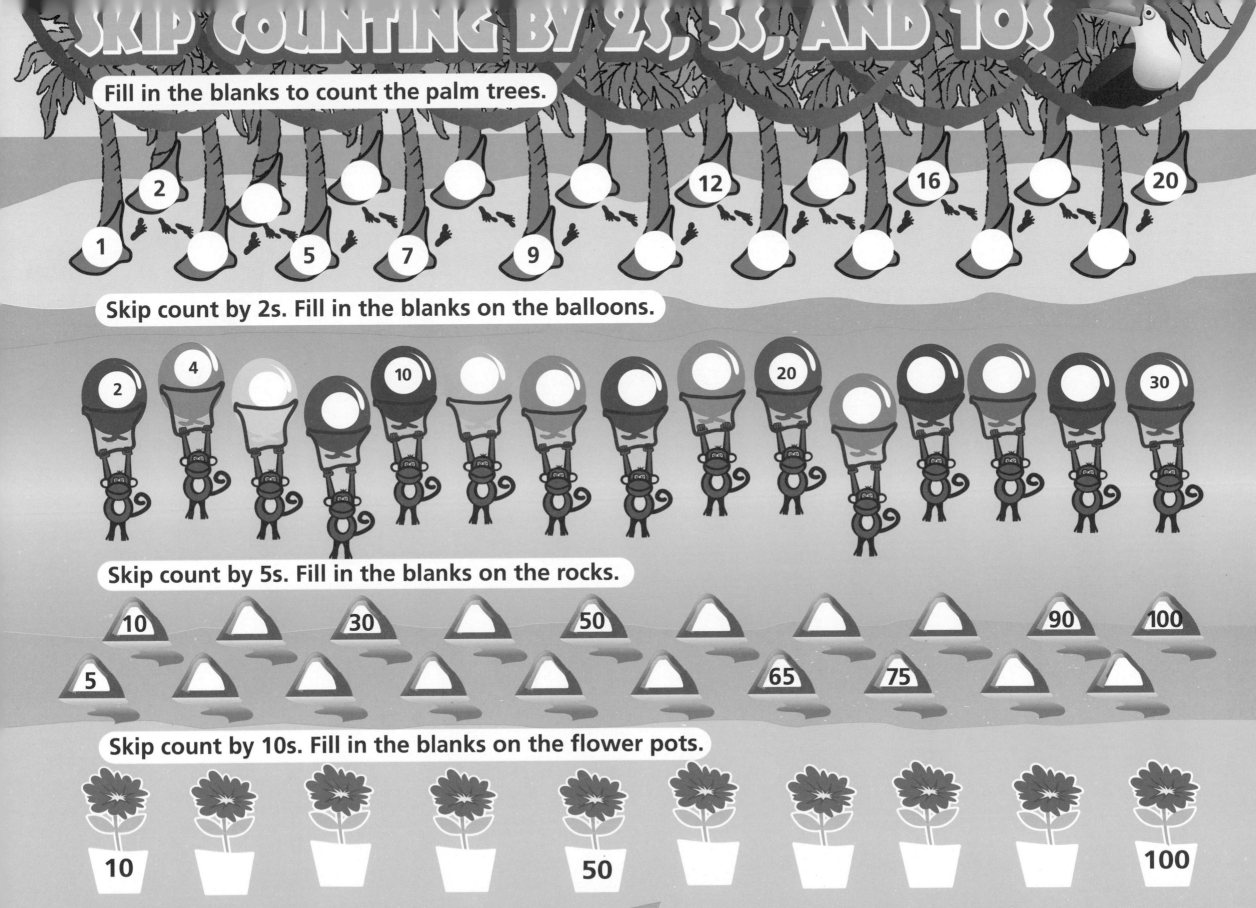

1 2 5 7 9 12 16 20

Skip count by 2s. Fill in the blanks on the balloons.

2 4 10 20 30

Skip count by 5s. Fill in the blanks on the rocks.

10 30 50 90 100

5 65 75

Skip count by 10s. Fill in the blanks on the flower pots.

10 50 100

Addition Puzzles

When you add, the answer is called the **sum**.

Using the sums, connect the dots from 1 to 20.

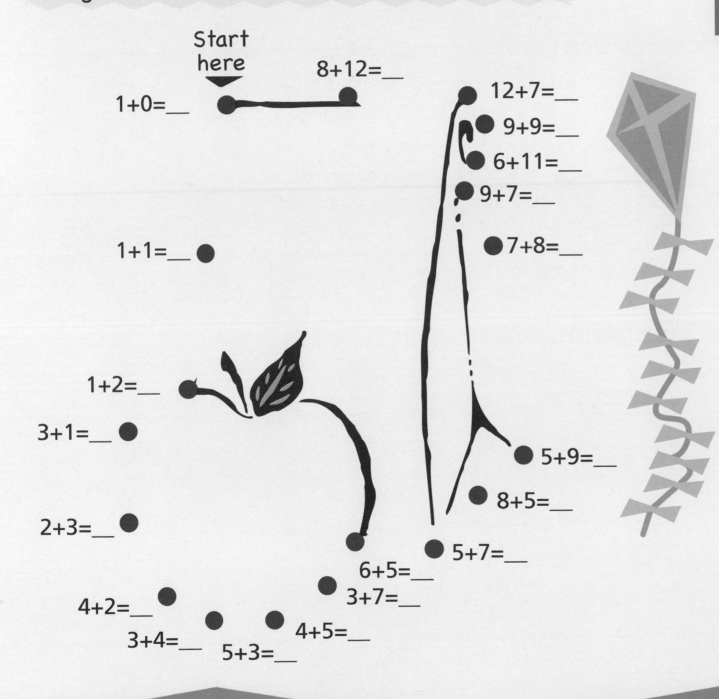

Start here

1+0=__

8+12=__

12+7=__

9+9=__

6+11=__

9+7=__

1+1=__

7+8=__

1+2=__

3+1=__

2+3=__

5+9=__

8+5=__

5+7=__

6+5=__

3+7=__

4+2=__

4+5=__

3+4=__

5+3=__

Addition of 2-digit numbers without regrouping.

Find the sums.

1. 24
   +32

6. 48
   +31

2. 13
   +46

7. 82
   + 6

3. 72
   +16

8. 53
   +25

4. 75
   +24

9. 17
   +22

5. 84
   +15

10.   4
    +63

3

Addition

How fast can you finish these icecream cones?

Add each number to the one beside it.
Put the answer below where the arrows point. The example is done for you.

Example

6	3	9	4	7
9	12	13	11	
	21	25	24	
		46	49	
			95	

1

9	7	5	3	1

2

2	6	7	9	5

3

12	14	16	15	17

Division is Dynamite

Division is equal sharing or groupings.
The answer to your division question is called a **quotient**.
Remember, ÷ means "divided into."

This shows 20 baseballs.

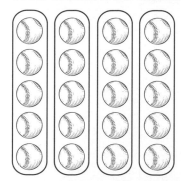

Divide the baseballs into groups of 5.
How many groups are there? ____4____
This shows 20 ÷ 4 = ____5____
This is a multiplication and
division fact family: 5 x 4 = 20
$\qquad\qquad\qquad$ 4 x 5 = 20
$\qquad\qquad\qquad$ 20 ÷ 5 = 4
$\qquad\qquad\qquad$ 20 ÷ 4 = 5

Try the following questions on your own!

1. Circle in groups of 3.

How many are there in total?

_____

How many groups of 3 are there?

_____

Write a division sentence.

_____

2. Circle in groups of 4.

How many are there in total?

_____

How many groups of 4?

_____

Write a division sentence.

_____

3. Circle in groups of 2.

How many are there in total?

_____

How many groups of 2?

_____

Write a division sentence.

_____

Write a division sentence to match each group.

4. 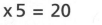 ____÷____=____

5. ____÷____=____

6. ____÷____=____

7. ____÷____=____

8. ____÷____=____

9

GRAPHS

Pictograph

A **pictograph** is a graph that uses pictures or symbols to show data.

Look at the graph and answer the questions.

Favourite drinks of a soccer team	
	Each glass stands for 1 soccer player.
Apple juice	
Orange juice	
Grape juice	
Water	

1. What drink did most soccer players vote for?

   Apple juice ⬜   Orange juice ⬜   Grape juice ⬛   Water ⬜

2. How many soccer players voted for orange juice?

   1   2   3   4   5

3. How many soccer players voted for water?

   1   2   3   4   5

4. How many soccer players voted all together?

   2   4   5   10   15

Create your own pie chart

A **pie chart** uses slices of a circle (or pie) to show data.

Ask six people which fruit they prefer: apple, banana, or orange. For each vote, colour one slice of the pie. Colour the slice red for every apple vote. Colour the slice yellow for every banana vote. Colour the slice orange for every orange vote.

Each slice stands for one person.

Legend:
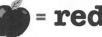 = red

 = yellow

 = orange

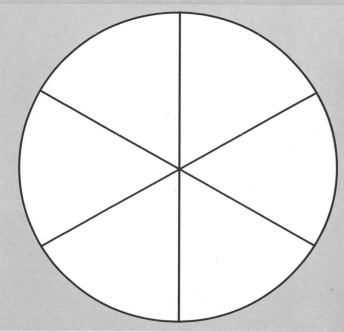

Look at your graph. Circle the answer to each question.

1. What fruit got the most votes?

2. What fruit got the fewest votes?

3. How many people voted for oranges?

   1   2   3   4   5   6

4. How many people voted for bananas?

   1   2   3   4   5   6

10

Money Maze

Colour the even-numbered beads orange. Colour the odd-numbered beads blue. Some are done.

0 1 2 3 4 5 6 7 8 9 10 11 12 13 14 15 16 17 18 19 20

Skip Count Dot to Dot

Skip count by 2s from 2 to 100.

Start
100 6 8
98 4
2
96 94 10
92 12 14
90 16
88 84
86 72 24
82 38
70 36
80 74 40 22
76 26
20
68 42 34 18
78
66 32 28
44
64 46 30
62 48
50
60
58 52
56 54
11

Pattern Maze

Follow this pattern through the maze.

Start

More! More! More!

Continue each pattern.

2, 4, 6,

A B B A

1,2,4,7,11,16,

Time

Write the time two ways.

 _____ o'clock
_____ : _____

 quarter _____ _____
_____ : _____

 quarter _____ _____
_____ : _____

 _____ thirty
_____ : _____

Draw the clock hands

Anna started skipping at 3:00. She stopped at 3:15.
Draw the times on the clocks.

 Started

 Stopped

Nico put the cake into the oven at 1:45.
It baked for one hour. Draw the times.

 Started

 **Stopped**

Write the times another way.

 [_____ : _____]

 [_____ : _____]

 [_____ : _____]

 [_____ : _____]

Circle the correct answer. The clock says  and it is dark outside. Is it: **midnight** or **noon**.

What does Tom need?

The calendar says

January
✗ ✗ ✗
✗
16

The thermometer says

Circle the things that Tom needs.

Temperature

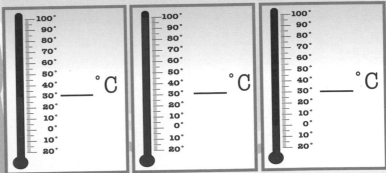

Temperature tells how hot or cold something is. We measure temperature with a thermometer. We tell the temperature using degrees Celsius (°C).

Write the temperature.

 _____ °C   _____ °C   _____ °C

HOT AND COLD

Water turns to ice at 0°. It is cold.

 **0°C**

Water boils at 100°. It is hot.

 **100°C**

A nice warm day at the beach is 25°C. It is warm.

25°C

Circle the correct temperature.

  100° C   25° C   0° C

  100° C   25° C   0° C

  100° C   25° C   0° C

Simon Says Following instructions

Play Simon Says by following the instructions for each picture. Remember, don't do it if it doesn't say 'Simon says'!

1. Simon says draw green spots on the turtle's back.
2. Simon says colour the turtle's feet yellow.
3. Simon says write a name for the turtle above the picture.
4. Draw an orange ribbon around the turtle's neck.

1. Simon says draw a circle in the box.
2. Simon says draw two eyes, a nose, and a mouth on the circle.
3. Draw green spots on the face.
4. Simon says draw blue spots on the face.

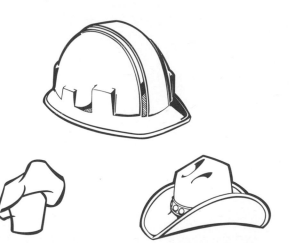

1. Draw a yellow circle around the smallest hat.
2. Simon says put a red X on the smallest hat.
3. Simon says colour the medium-size hat green.
4. Simon says put a box around the two largest hats.

1. Simon says trace the triangle with blue.
2. Simon says draw two small yellow circles inside the triangle.
3. Draw a red box around the triangle.
4. Simon says draw ears on the triangle.

More Simon Says

Simon says number the mixed up sentences to show the correct order.

- [ ] I come back inside and hang up my wet coat and pants.
- [ ] I run outside to splash in the puddles.
- [ ] I look out the window and see the rain.
- [ ] I put on my raincoat, rain pants, and boots.
- [ ] My friend comes to jump in the puddles with me.

Simon says draw a picture of you and a friend jumping in puddles on a rainy day.

A Postcard

Postcard Basics

A postcard has a picture on one side and a short note on the other. You might send one when you go on a trip.

July 9, 20XX

Dear Anna,

    I am having fun at camp. One day I saw a deer and a fox! We had a campfire. See you next Sunday!

Your friend,

Pina

Anna Banana
123 Home Street
Mytown, ON
L0L P0P

Greeting
Start with a capital. Put a comma after the person's name.

Today's Date

Body
Tell about camp here. Indent the first line.

Address
The post office will deliver your postcard to the address you put here.

Your Name

Closing
Use a capital on the first word only. End with a comma.

Write Your Own

Write a note on the postcard to someone about a place you have been to or want to go. Then draw a picture for the front of the postcard.

_____ ,

_____

_____

_____

_____ To: _____

_____

_____ ,

_____

Amazing Adjectives!

Circle the adjective.

 (happy) boy   sad boy

 big dog   little dog

 tall house   small house

 green leaves   red leaves

 one egg   two eggs

 tiny rock   huge rock

 more cake   less cake

---

An **adjective** describes a person, place, or thing. It tells what the noun is like. Examples:

big fish   **small** fish

 green socks    **red** socks

one hat   **three** hats

Circle adjectives in the story.

One (sunny) day, we went to the circus. It was in a huge, striped tent. I saw a tall clown who had a red nose, big shoes, and a funny hat. She drove a tiny blue car. She threw little candies to some happy children. I got three red ones. That was a great day!

Silly Sentences

Fill in the blanks with adjectives to make silly sentences.

Choose from the list or think of your own.

My dog has _____ ears and a _____ tail.

For lunch, I had a bowl of _____ soup, some _____ bread, and a drink of _____ juice.

For Halloween, my brother wore a _____ cape, _____ pants, and carried a _____ wand.

Adjective List

slimy	gooey	wet
green	noisy	crusty
striped	blue	short
hot	huge	long

Draw a picture of one of your sentences.

Synonyms

Choose a Synonym

Read the first word. Circle another word that is a synonym. The first one is done.

smile	lips	(grin)	frown
big	high	small	large
happy	glad	scared	small
angry	frown	mad	shy
laugh	chuckle	happy	funny
scared	brave	afraid	tall
quick	slow	race	speedy
small	flat	tiny	bumpy
thin	tall	long	slender
friend	pal	sister	mother
carpet	floor	blanket	rug
bravery	fear	courage	happiness

Synonyms are words that mean the same thing. **Fast** and **quick** are synonyms.

Build a Sentence

Read the sentences. Write a synonym for each underlined word. The first one is done for you. Answers will vary.

The <u>big</u> dog has <u>tiny</u> ears.
The <u>large</u> dog has <u>small</u> ears.

My <u>friend</u> <u>laughed</u> when she saw the clown.
My _____ _____ when she saw the clown.

The <u>slender</u> rope broke.
The _____ rope broke.

<u>Pick</u> your favourite colour.
_____ your favourite colour.

My brother was <u>scared</u> of the <u>small</u> spider.
My brother was _____ of the _____ spider.

Do you like the <u>thin</u> ribbon?
Do you like the _____ ribbon?

My bike needs to be <u>repaired</u>.
My bike needs to be _____.

Hint: **Synonym** and **same** both start with **s**. This helps us remember that **synonyms** mean the **same** thing.

Find the Synonyms

Put an S beside each pair of words that are synonyms. Put an X beside the pairs that are not synonyms. One is done.

fast	quick	S
tiny	smooth	_____
slender	skinny	_____
pal	friend	_____
rough	smooth	_____
tap	faucet	_____
scared	afraid	_____
rug	carpet	_____

24

Antonyms

Antonyms are words that mean the **opposite** of each other. **Fast** and **slow** are antonyms.

Antonyms

Draw a line from each word to its antonym. The first one is done for you.

rough	bottom
up	smooth
top	down
front	break
fix	back
day	night
after	quickly
to	from
slowly	before

Antonym PUZZLE

Fill in the puzzle with an antonym for each clue. The first one is done for you.

1. night   3. fix   5. slow
2. front   4. before   6. polite

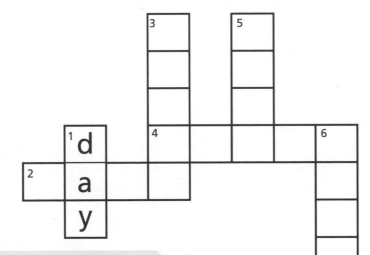

Synonyms and Antonyms

Put an S beside each pair of synonyms. Put an A beside each pair of antonyms. The first one is done.

beautiful	pretty	**S**
fancy	plain	_____
add	subtract	_____
rich	wealthy	_____
before	after	_____
scared	afraid	_____
polite	rude	_____
kind	helpful	_____
giggle	laugh	_____
no	yes	_____

Matching Antonyms

cry   laugh   big   small

Antonym Riddle

Q: What is the difference between here and there?

A: The letter T

25

These puzzles use 1, 2, 3, 4, 5, and 6.

Puzzle 1

	3		2	6	
6			3	1	5
2			5	3	1
1		3			6
3	1	5	6		
		6	1		3

Puzzle 2

	1	3		6	5
5	6	4			3
3	5		1		
		2		3	6
4	3		6	2	
6		1	3	5	

Puzzle 3

2				1	5
	5	4	2	6	3
		6	5		1
4	1	5	3	2	6
	4		6	3	
	3		1	5	4

Puzzle 4

		6	3	2	1
4	2		5	3	6
3	1			2	
2	5		1		3
		4	5	3	
6		2			1

Puzzle 5

		5	3		
3	4			6	
4	5		2	1	6
1		2		3	5
5	1	4			3
2		6		5	4

Puzzle 6

3	5		1	4	6
4				2	
6	1		4	3	2
2	4	3			1
5		4		1	3
1	3	6	2	5	

Puzzle 7

	4	2		3	
	6		1		2
6			5		
	3	4		2	1
5	6	3			4
	1	3	2	6	

Puzzle 8

5		2		4	6
	4	3		1	
3	6		1		4
	2				3
4	5	6	2		
	3	1	4	6	5

More SUDOKU

These puzzles use 1, 2, 3, 4, 5, 6, 7, 8, and 9!

Puzzle 1

2			4	5	7		9	1
4	9	8		2		3	7	5
5		7	8	3		6	2	
	2	4	3	6		1		9
		1	7		2	4		3
	5	3		9	4	7	6	
6	7		2	4		9		
3	8	9		1			2	4
1	4			7	8	5		6

Puzzle 2

3	9		8	1	5	4	6	
4		2		6		5	3	8
5	6	8		4	2		1	7
7	8	5		2		1	9	4
	2		1	9	4	7		
	4	9	5		8		2	3
	7	4	9		6	2		1
	5	6		8	1		7	9
9			2	5			4	6

Puzzle 3

7		3	4		2	6	5	8
	2		8			3	7	4
4	8	6	5	3		1		2
8		5	2	7	9	4	1	6
	6	4		8	3			5
1	7		6	5		8		9
		8		1	5		6	7
6	9			2			4	3
3	5		9	4		2		

Puzzle 4

7		6	2	5	1	3	4	9
		4	6	7	9	8		
9	1	2	8		4	7		6
8	9		4	2	3			5
	6		9		7	1	2	3
2	3	7	5			9		4
6	2	9	7		8	5	3	1
		7	3	1		4	9	
1	4		3	9		2		7

Puzzle 5

		1	6	2	3	8	7	9
3	6	7				1		5
8	9	2	5	1	7		4	6
2		6	8		1	9	5	7
5	8	4	7		9	2		
7		9	2	5	6	4	8	
	7	3		8	2			4
9		5	1	7	4	6		8
1	4		3	6	5		9	2

Puzzle 6

	6	5	7	9	4		1	2
3				2	5	6		
	2	1	8	6	3	4	9	5
6	8	7	5	1		9	4	3
5	4	3	6	8	9	1	2	
2		9		3	7	5		6
4	7			5		8	6	9
		6	2	4				1
1	3		9	7	6	2	5	4

ABCDEFGHIJKLMNOPQRSTUVWXYZ

A A A

B B B

C C C

D D D

E E E

F F F

G G G

H H H

I I I

J J J

K K K

L L L

M M M

N N N

O O O

P P P

Q Q Q

R R R

S S S

T T T

U U U

V V V

W W W

X X X

Y Y Y

Z Z Z

Practice each letter.

a b c d e f g h i j k l m n o p q r s t u v w x y z

a a a

b b b

c c c

d d d

e e e

f f f

g g g

h h h

i i i

j j j

k k k

l l l

m m m

n n n

o o o

p p p

q q q

r r r

s s s

t t t

u u u

v v v

w w w

x x x

y y y

z z z

Trace each letter.

a b c d e f g h i j k l m n o p q r s t u v w x y z

A B C D E F G H I J K L M N O P Q R S T U V W X Y Z

a a a
b b b
c c c
d d d
e e e
f f f
g g g
h h h
i i i
j j j
k k k
l l l
m m m
n n n

o o o
p p p
q q q
r r r
s s s
t t t
u u u
v v v
w w w
x x x
y y y
z z z

A A A
B B B
C C C
D D D
E E E
F F F
G G G
H H H
I I I
J J J
K K K
L L L
M M M
N N N

O O O
P P P
Q Q Q
R R R
S S S
T T T
U U U
V V V
W W W
X X X
Y Y Y
Z Z Z

Skip Counting - Page 2

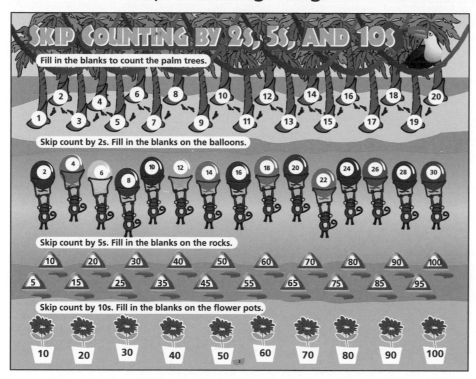

Play with Place Value- Page 3

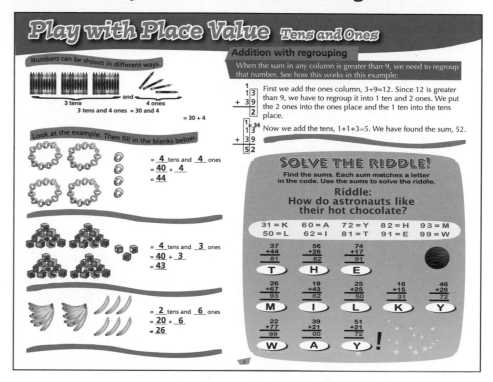

Addition - Page 4

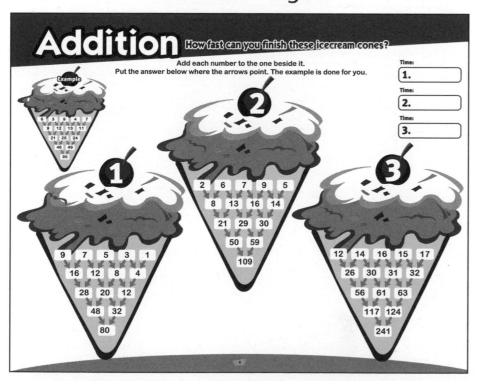

Addition Puzzles - Page 5

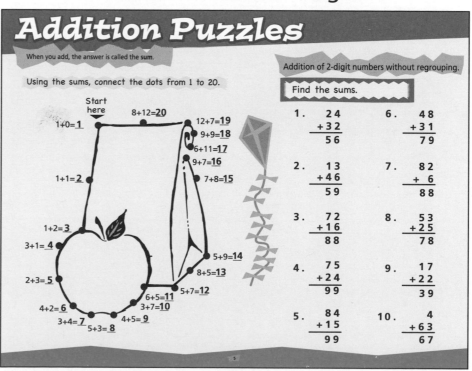